MINI
A DOZEN A SONGBOOK

Christmas

Including Away In A Manger, Jingle Bells,
Walking In The Air plus many more…

© Copyright 2014 The Willis Music Company
Florence, Kentucky, USA. All Rights Reserved.

Exclusive Distributors:
Music Sales Limited
Newmarket Road, Bury St Edmunds, Suffolk IP33 3YB, UK.
Music Sales Pty Limited
Units 3-4, 17 Willfox Street, Condell Park, NSW 2200, Australia.

Order No. WMR101365
ISBN: 978-1-78305-641-5

Arrangements, engravings and audio supplied by Camden Music Services.
CD audio arranged, programmed and mixed by Jeremy Birchall and Christopher Hussey.
Edited by Sam Lung.

Printed in the EU.

THE WILLIS MUSIC COMPANY

The *A Dozen A Day Songbook* series contains wonderful easy Christmas favorites that may be used as companion pieces to the memorable technique exercises in the *A Dozen A Day* series. They are also suitable as supplements with ANY piano method!

The included CD provides fully-orchestrated demonstration and backing tracks for a fun play-along experience!

Contents

Good King Wenceslas

Use with A Dozen A Day Mini Book, after Group I (page 8)

Words by John Mason Neale
Music Traditional Finnish
Arranged by Christopher Hussey

TRACKS 1–2

Confidently

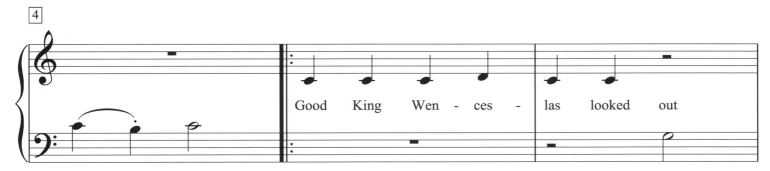

Good King Wen - ces - las looked out

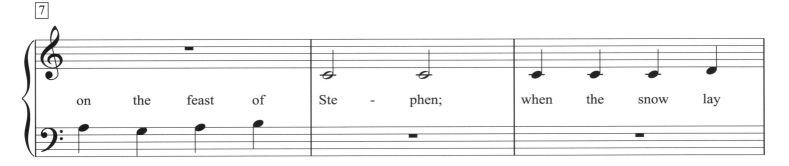

on the feast of Ste - phen; when the snow lay

Accompaniment (student plays one octave higher than written)

Confidently

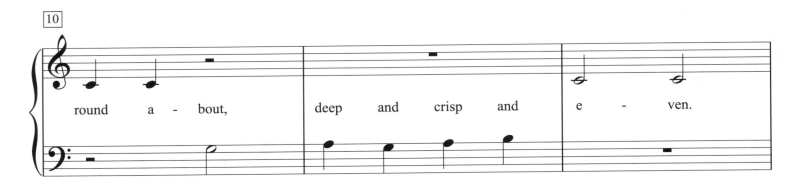

round a - bout, deep and crisp and e - ven.

Bright - ly shone the moon that night, though the frost was

cru - el; when a poor man came in sight,

gath - 'ring   win - ter   fu - - - el.

O Come, All Ye Faithful

Use after Group I (page 8)

Words & Music by John Francis Wade
Arranged by Christopher Hussey

 TRACKS 3–4

Majestically

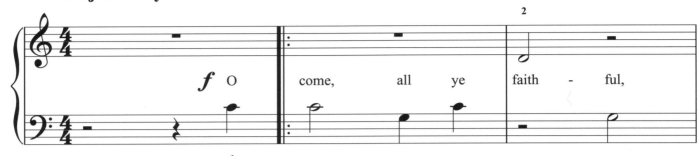

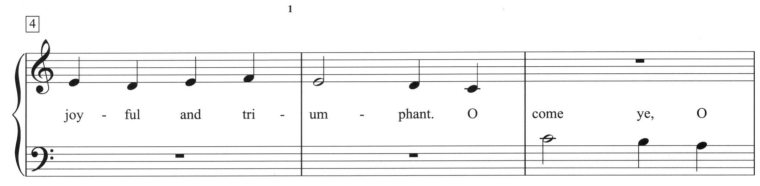

Accompaniment (student plays one octave higher than written)

Majestically

© Copyright 2014 The Willis Music Company, USA.
All Rights Reserved. International Copyright Secured.

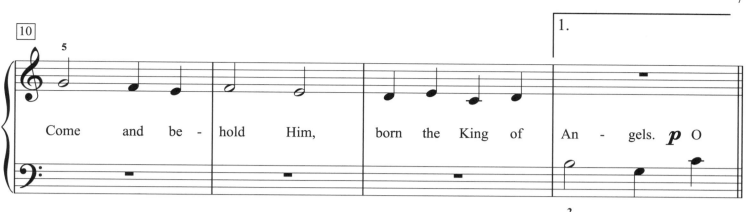

Come and be - hold Him, born the King of An - gels. *p* O

come, let us a - dore Him, O come let us a -

- dore Him, *f* O come let us a - dore Him,____

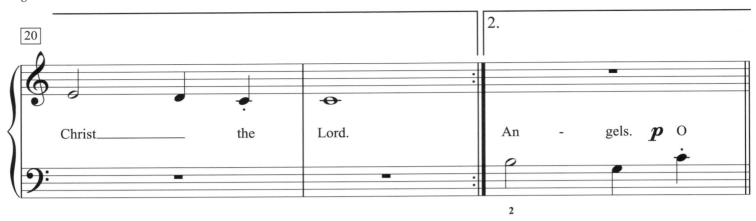

Christ_____ the Lord. An - gels. *p* O

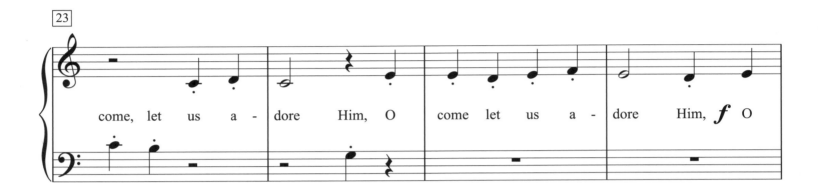

come, let us a - dore Him, O come let us a - dore Him, *f* O

come let us a - dore Him,_____ Christ_____ the Lord.

God Rest Ye Merry, Gentlemen

Use after Group II (page 12)

Traditional English
Arranged by Christopher Hussey

**TRACKS
5–6**

Flowingly

rest ye mer - ry, gen - tle - men, let noth - ing you dis -

Accompaniment (student plays one octave higher than written)

Flowingly

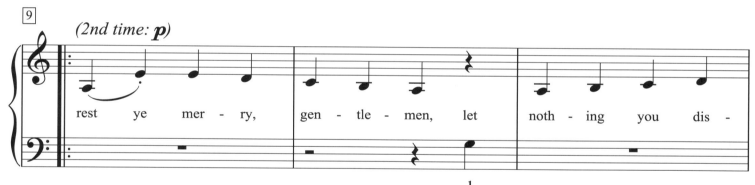

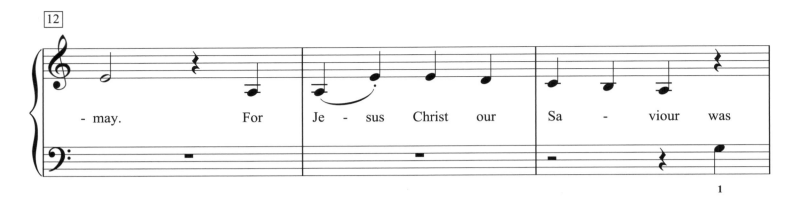

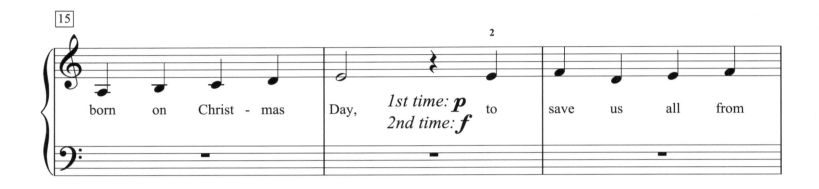

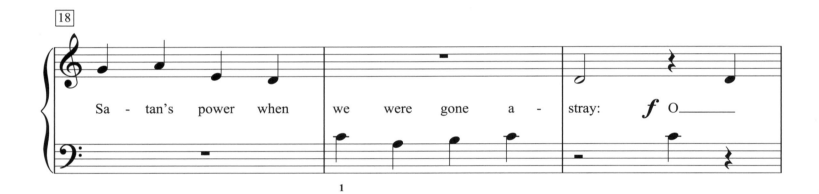

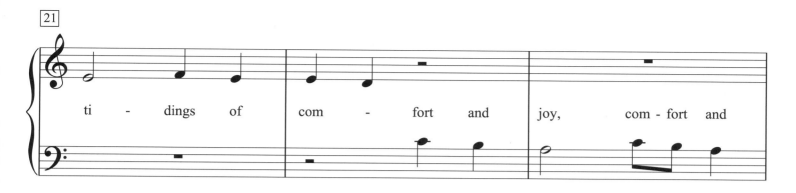

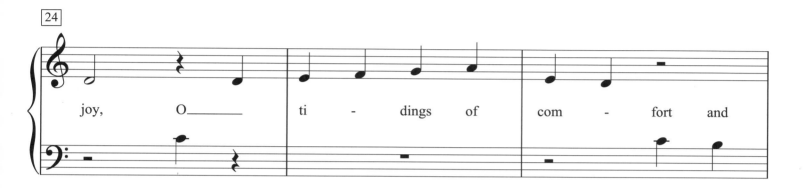

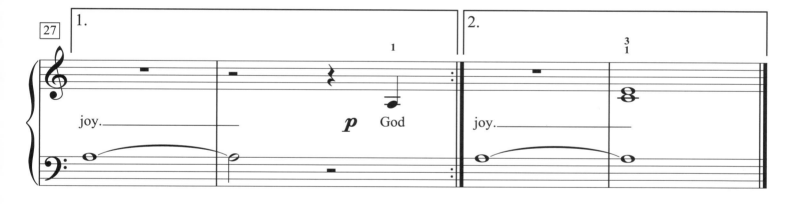

In The Bleak Midwinter

Use after Group II (page 12)

Words by Christina Rossetti
Music by Gustav Holst
Arranged by Christopher Hussey

TRACKS 7–8

Tenderly

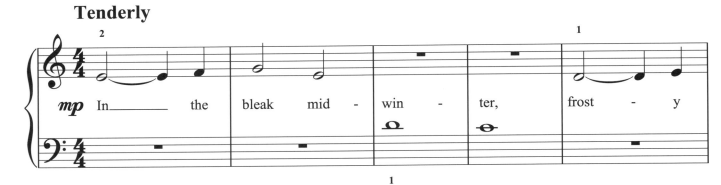

In_____ the bleak mid - win - ter, frost - y

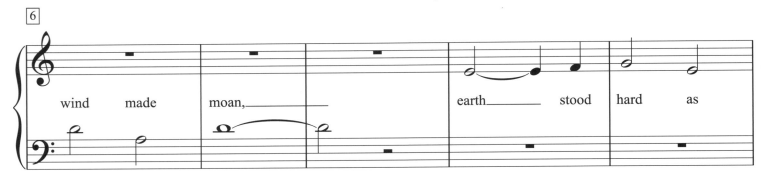

wind made moan,_____ earth_____ stood hard as

i - ron, wa - ter like_____ a stone._____

Accompaniment (student plays one octave higher than written)

Tenderly

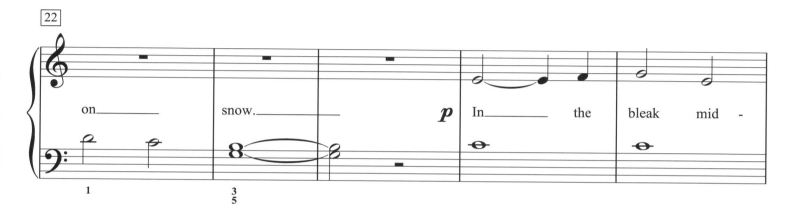

We Three Kings Of Orient Are

Use after Group III (page 16)

Words & Music by John Henry Hopkins
Arranged by Christopher Hussey

**TRACKS
9–10**

Smoothly

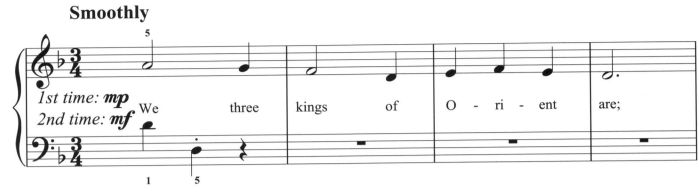

1st time: **mp**
2nd time: **mf**
We three kings of O - ri - ent are;

bear - ing gifts we trav - el a - far.

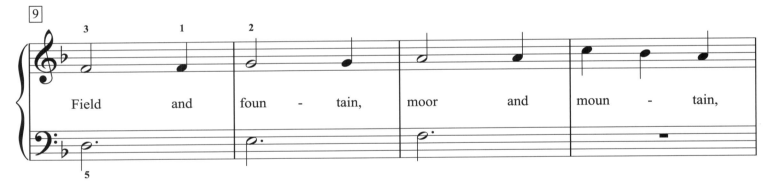

Field and foun - tain, moor and moun - tain,

Accompaniment (student plays one octave higher than written)

Smoothly

1st time: **mp**
2nd time: **mf**

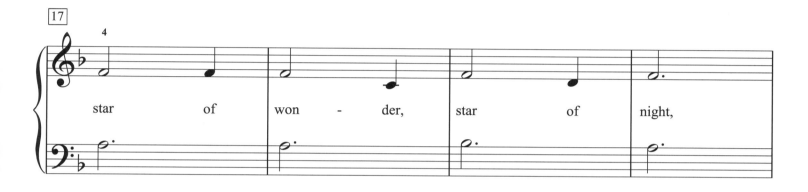

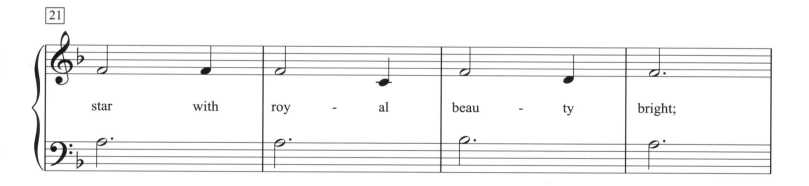

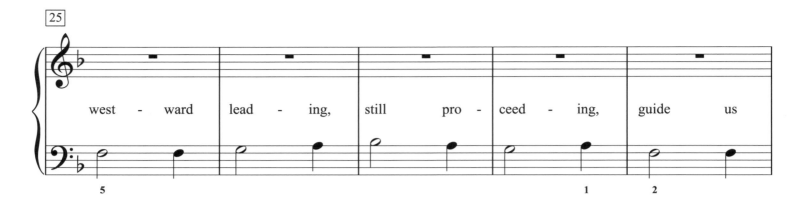

west - ward lead - ing, still pro - ceed - ing, guide us

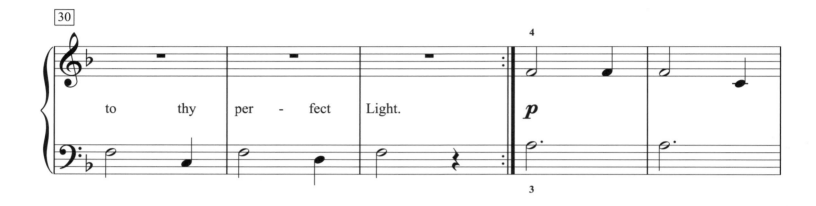

to thy per - fect Light.

Away In A Manger

Use after Group III (page 16)

Words Traditional
Music by William Kirkpatrick
Arranged by Christopher Hussey

TRACKS 11–12

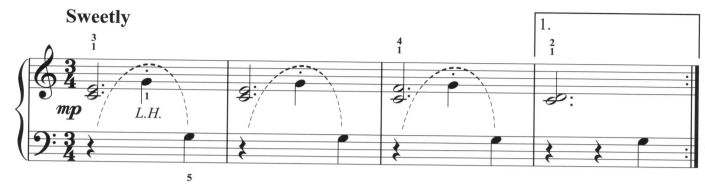

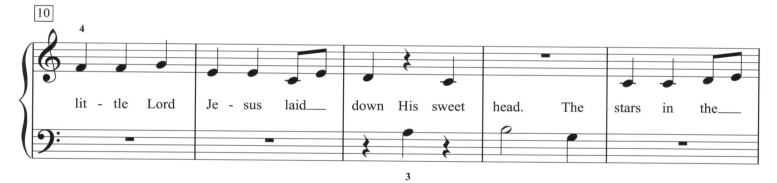

Accompaniment (student plays one octave higher than written)

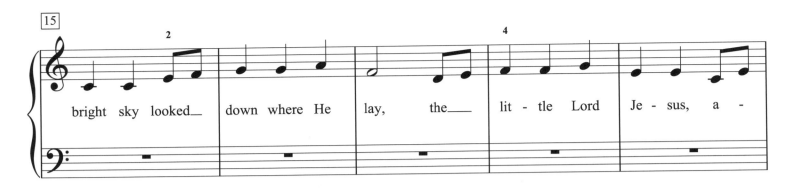

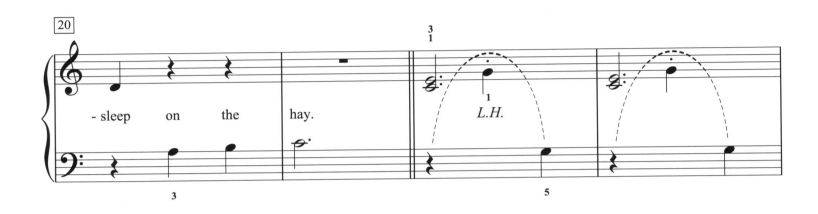

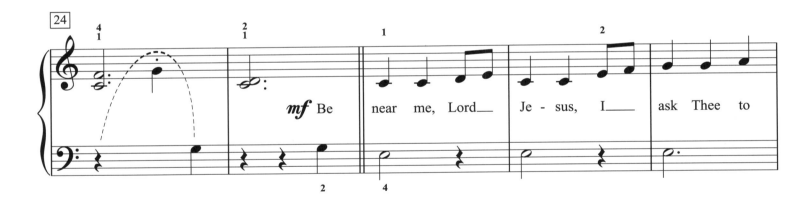

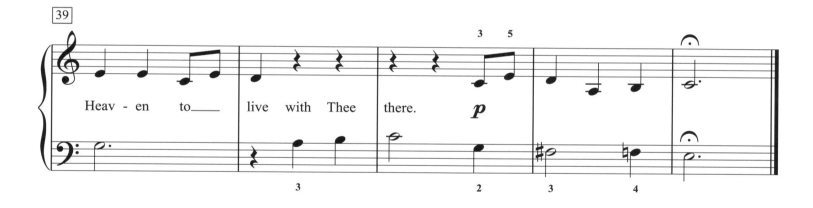

Rocking Carol

Use after Group IV (page 20)

Words by Percy Dearmer
Music Traditional Czech
Arranged by Christopher Hussey

TRACKS
13–14

Gently, with expression

Lit - tle Ba - by, sweet - ly___ sleep, do not___ stir; we will___ lend a___

coat of___ fur. We will rock You, rock You, rock___ You, we will rock You,

Accompaniment (student plays one octave higher than written)

Gently, with expression

rock You, rock__ You. See the fur to keep You__ warm, snug - ly__ round Your__

ti - ny__ form.

Walking In The Air

Theme from THE SNOWMAN

Use after Group IV (page 20)

Words & Music by Howard Blake
Arranged by Christopher Hussey

TRACKS 15–16

Steadily, in a singing style

We're

walk-ing in the air,⎯⎯⎯ we're float-ing in the moon - lit
hold-ing ve-ry tight,⎯⎯⎯ I'm ri - ding in the mid - night

sky;⎯⎯⎯ the peo-ple far be - low are
blue;⎯⎯⎯ I'm find-ing I can fly so

Accompaniment (student plays one octave higher than written)

Steadily, in a singing style

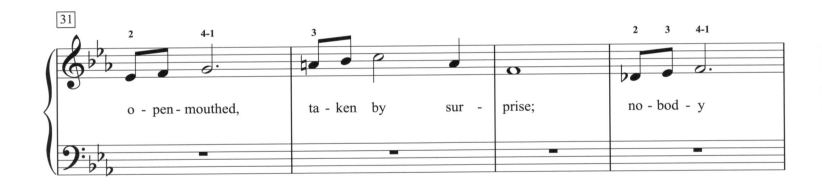

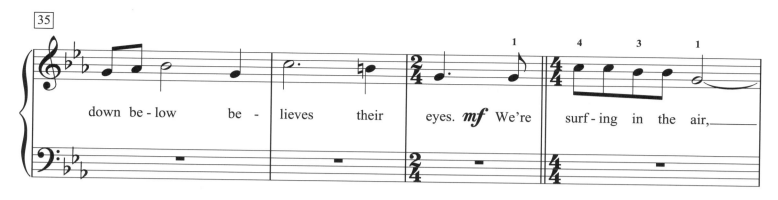

down be - low   be - lieves   their   eyes. *mf* We're   surf - ing   in   the   air,___

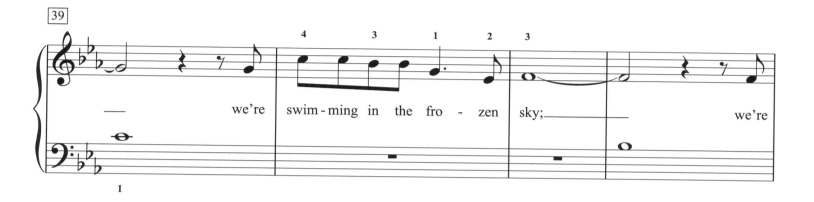

___   we're   swim - ming   in   the   fro - zen   sky;___   we're

drift - ing   o - ver   i - cy   moun - tains   float - ing   by.___   *p*

Jingle Bells

Use after Group V (page 24)

Words & Music by James Lord Pierpont
Arranged by Christopher Hussey

TRACKS
17–18

Lightly, with a bounce

Jing - le bells, jing - le bells, jing - le all the way,

oh, what fun it is to ride in a one - horse o - pen sleigh._____

Accompaniment (student plays one octave higher than written)

Lightly, with a bounce

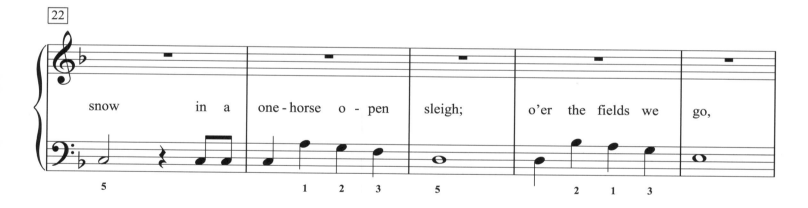

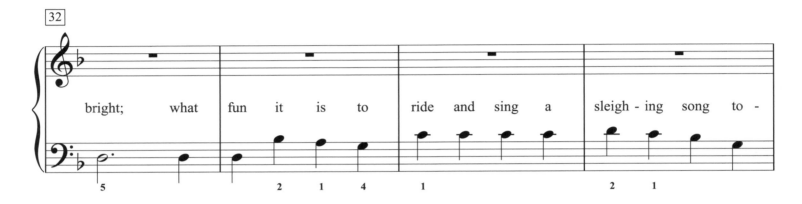

All I Want For Christmas Is You

Use after Group V (page 24)

Words & Music by Mariah Carey & Walter Afanasieff
Arranged by Christopher Hussey

TRACKS 19–20

I don't want a lot___ for Christ-mas, there is just one thing I need,___ and

I don't care a-bout___ the pres-ents un-der-neath___ the Christ-mas tree.___

Accompaniment (student plays one octave higher than written)

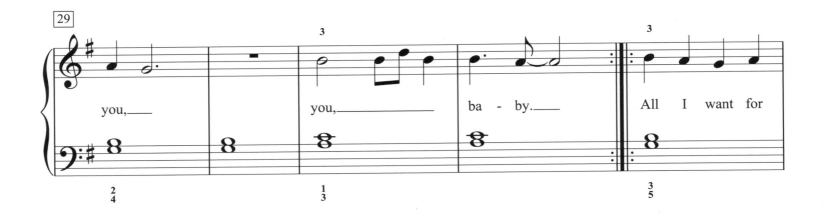

123456789